Chopin
2010

WYDANIE NARODOWE
DZIEŁ FRYDERYKA CHOPINA

NATIONAL EDITION
OF THE WORKS OF FRYDERYK CHOPIN

POLONAISE in E♭ Op. 22
preceded with ANDANTE SPIANATO
FOR PIANO AND ORCHESTRA
Score

NATIONAL EDITION
Edited by JAN EKIER

Foundation
for the National Edition
of the Works of Fryderyk Chopin

PWM
EDITION

SERIES A. WORKS PUBLISHED DURING CHOPIN'S LIFETIME. VOLUME XVf

FRYDERYK CHOPIN

POLONEZ Es-dur Op. 22
poprzedzony ANDANTE SPIANATO
NA FORTEPIAN I ORKIESTRĘ

Partytura

WYDANIE NARODOWE
Redaktor naczelny: JAN EKIER

FUNDACJA WYDANIA NARODOWEGO
POLSKIE WYDAWNICTWO MUZYCZNE SA
WARSZAWA 2018

SERIA A. UTWORY WYDANE ZA ŻYCIA CHOPINA. TOM XVf

Redakcja tomu: Jan Ekier, Paweł Kamiński

Komentarz wykonawczy i Komentarz źródłowy (skrócony) dołączone są do nut głównej
serii *Wydania Narodowego* oraz do strony internetowej www.chopin-nationaledition.com

Pełne *Komentarze źródłowe* do poszczególnych tomów będą publikowane oddzielnie.

Wydany w oddzielnym tomie *Wstęp do Wydania Narodowego Dzieł Fryderyka Chopina
– 1. Zagadnienia edytorskie* obejmuje całokształt ogólnych problemów wydawniczych,
zaś *Wstęp… – 2. Zagadnienia wykonawcze* – całokształt ogólnych problemów interpretacyjnych.
Pierwsza część *Wstępu* jest także dostępna na stronie www.pwm.com.pl

Polonez w autentycznym układzie na jeden fortepian tworzy tom 16 **A XIVb**,
a wersja z wyciągiem fortepianowym znajduje się w tomie *Utwory koncertowe* 32 **B VII**.

Głosy orkiestrowe dostępne do wypożyczenia w Bibliotece Materiałów Orkiestrowych PWM,
ul. Fredry 8, 00-097 Warszawa, tel. 22 635-35-50 / fax 22 826-97-80
www.pwm.com.pl / e-mail: bmo@pwm.com.pl

Editors of this Volume: Jan Ekier, Paweł Kamiński

A *Performance Commentary* and a *Source Commentary (abridged)* are included in the
music of the main series of the *National Edition* and available on www.chopin-nationaledition.com

Full *Source Commentaries* on each volume will be published separately.

The *Introduction to the National Edition of the Works of Fryderyk Chopin
1. Editorial Problems*, published as a separate volume, covers general matters concerning the publication.
The *Introduction… 2. Problems of Performance* covers all general questions of the interpretation.
First part of the *Introduction* is also available on the website www.pwm.com.pl

Polonaise in authentic arrangement for one piano makes up volume 16 **A XIVb**, and the version with the piano arrangement
is to be found in the volume *Concert Works* 32 **B VII**.

Orchestral parts can be borrowed from the Library of Orchestral Materials of the PWM Edition,
Fredry 8, 00-097 Warszawa, tel. + 48 22 635-35-50 / fax + 48 22 826-97-80
www.pwm.com.pl / e-mail: bmo@pwm.com.pl

Polonez Es-dur op. 22 / Polonaise in E♭ major Op. 22

ANDANTE SPIANATO

page / s. 11

POLONAISE

page / s. 14

about the Polonaise ...

Op. 22

"I started writing a Polonaise for piano and orchestra, but it only gins; there is a ginning but no beginning."

From F. Chopin's letter to Tytus Woyciechowski in Poturzyn, Warsaw, 18 September 1830.

o Polonezie ...

op. 22

„Zacząłem Poloneza z orkiestrą, ale tylko dopiero się cznie, jest czątek, ale początku nie ma."

Z listu F. Chopina do Tytusa Woyciechowskiego w Poturzynie, Warszawa 18 IX 1830.

ORCHESTRA

2 Flauti

2 Oboi

2 Clarinetti in si♭

2 Fagotti

2 Corni in fa

Trombone

Timpani in mi♭, si♭

Violini I

Violini II

Viole

Violoncelli

Contrabassi

Grande polonaise brillante
A Madame d'Est

pour le piano avec accompagnement d'orchestre, précédée d'un Andante spianato

ANDANTE SPIANATO

op. 22

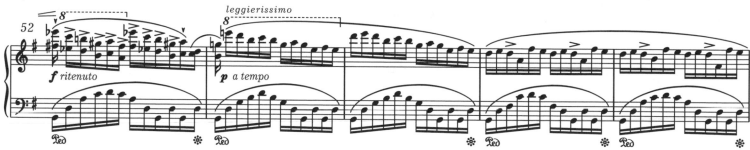

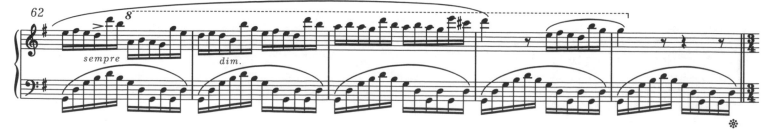

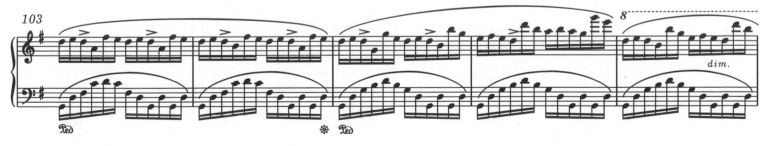

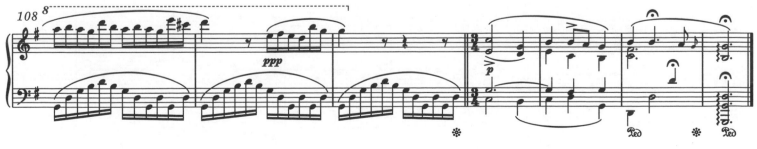

POLONAISE

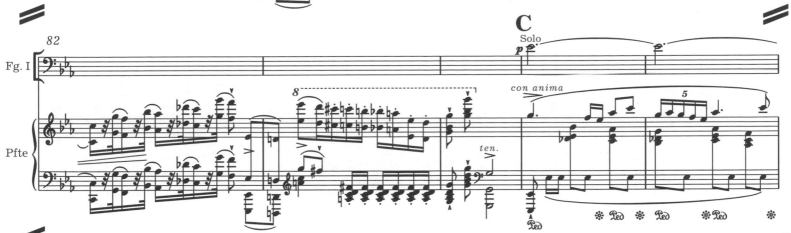

20

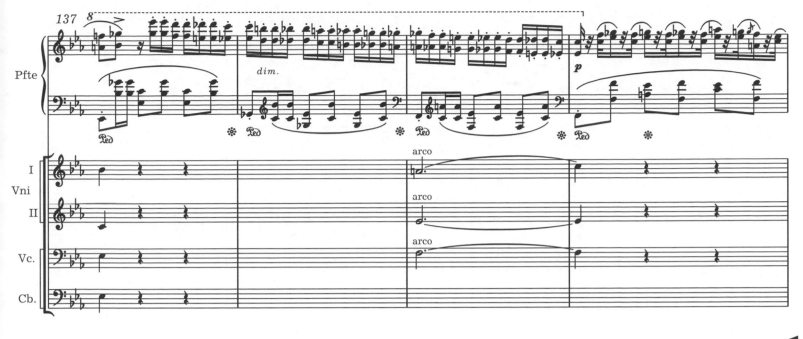

24

Okładka i opracowanie graficzne · Cover design and graphics: MARIA EKIER
Tłumaczenie angielskie · English translation: ALEKSADRA RODZIŃSKA-CHOJNOWSKA

Fundacja Wydania Narodowego Dzieł Fryderyka Chopina
ul. Okólnik 2, pok. 405, 00-368 Warszawa
www.chopin-nationaledition.com

Polskie Wydawnictwo Muzyczne SA
al. Krasińskiego 11a, Kraków
www.pwm.com.pl

Wyd. I. Printed in Poland 2018. Drukarnia REGIS Sp. z o.o.
05-230 Kobyłka, ul. Napoleona 4

ISMN M-9013328-7-4

NATIONAL EDITION OF THE WORKS OF FRYDERYK CHOPIN

Plan of the edition

Series A. WORKS PUBLISHED DURING CHOPIN'S LIFETIME

1	**A I**	**Ballades** Opp. 23, 38, 47, 52
2	**A II**	**Etudes** Opp. 10, 25, Three Etudes (Méthode des Méthodes)
3	**A III**	**Impromptus** Opp. 29, 36, 51
4	**A IV**	**Mazurkas (A)** Opp. 6, 7, 17, 24, 30, 33, 41, Mazurka in a (Gaillard), Mazurka in a (from the album La France Musicale /Notre Temps/), Opp. 50, 56, 59, 63
5	**A V**	**Nocturnes** Opp. 9, 15, 27, 32, 37, 48, 55, 62
6	**A VI**	**Polonaises (A)** Opp. 26, 40, 44, 53, 61
7	**A VII**	**Preludes** Opp. 28, 45
8	**A VIII**	**Rondos** Opp. 1, 5, 16
9	**A IX**	**Scherzos** Opp. 20, 31, 39, 54
10	**A X**	**Sonatas** Opp. 35, 58
11	**A XI**	**Waltzes (A)** Opp. 18, 34, 42, 64
12	**A XII**	**Various Works (A)** Variations brillantes Op. 12, Bolero, Tarantella, Allegro de concert, Fantaisie Op. 49, Berceuse, Barcarolle; *supplement* – Variation VI from "Hexameron"
13	**A XIIIa**	**Concerto in E minor** Op. 11 for piano and orchestra (version for one piano)
14	**A XIIIb**	**Concerto in F minor** Op. 21 for piano and orchestra (version for one piano)
15	**A XIVa**	**Concert Works** for piano and orchestra Opp. 2, 13, 14 (version for one piano)
16	**A XIVb**	**Grande Polonaise in E♭ major** Op. 22 for piano and orchestra (version for one piano)
17	**A XVa**	**Variations on "Là ci darem" from "Don Giovanni"** Op. 2. Score
18	**A XVb**	**Concerto in E minor** Op. 11. Score (historical version)
19	**A XVc**	**Fantasia on Polish Airs** Op. 13. Score
20	**A XVd**	**Krakowiak** Op. 14. Score
21	**A XVe**	**Concerto in F minor** Op. 21. Score (historical version)
22	**A XVf**	**Grande Polonaise in E♭ major** Op. 22. Score
23	**A XVI**	**Works for Piano and Cello** Polonaise Op. 3, Grand Duo Concertant, Sonata Op. 65
24	**A XVII**	**Piano Trio** Op. 8

Series B. WORKS PUBLISHED POSTHUMOUSLY

(The titles in square brackets [] have been reconstructed by the National Edition; the titles in slant marks // are still in use today but are definitely, or very probably, not authentic)

25	**B I**	**Mazurkas (B)** in B♭, G, a, C, F, G, B♭, A♭, C, a, g, f
26	**B II**	**Polonaises (B)** in B♭, g, A♭, g♯, d, f, b♭, B♭, G♭
27	**B III**	**Waltzes (B)** in E, b, D♭, A♭, e, G♭, A♭, f, a
28	**B IV**	**Various Works (B)** Variations in E, Sonata in c (Op. 4)
29	**B V**	**Various Compositions** Funeral March in c, [Variants] /Souvenir de Paganini/, Nocturne in e, Ecossaises in D, G, D♭, Contredanse, [Allegretto], Lento con gran espressione /Nocturne in c♯/, Cantabile in B♭, Presto con leggierezza /Prelude in A♭/, Impromptu in c♯ /Fantaisie-Impromptu/, "Spring" (version for piano), Sostenuto /Waltz in E♭/, Moderato /Feuille d'Album/, Galop Marquis, Nocturne in c
30	**B VIa**	**Concerto in E minor** Op. 11 for piano and orchestra (version with second piano)
31	**B VIb**	**Concerto in F minor** Op. 21 for piano and orchestra (version with second piano)
32	**B VII**	**Concert Works** for piano and orchestra Opp. 2, 13, 14, 22 (version with second piano)
33	**B VIIIa**	**Concerto in E minor** Op. 11. Score (concert version)
34	**B VIIIb**	**Concerto in F minor** Op. 21. Score (concert version)
35	**B IX**	**Rondo in C** for two pianos; **Variations in D** for four hands; *addendum* – working version of Rondo in C (for one piano)
36	**B X**	**Songs**

37	**Supplement**	Compositions partly by Chopin: Hexameron, Mazurkas in F♯, D, D, C, Variations for Flute and Piano; harmonizations of songs and dances: "The Dąbrowski Mazurka", "God who hast embraced Poland" (Largo) Bourrées in G, A, Allegretto in A-major/minor

WYDANIE NARODOWE DZIEŁ FRYDERYKA CHOPINA

Plan edycji

Seria A. UTWORY WYDANE ZA ŻYCIA CHOPINA

Seria B. UTWORY WYDANE POŚMIERTNIE

(Tytuły w nawiasach kwadratowych [] są tytułami zrekonstruowanymi przez WN, tytuły w nawiasach prostych // są dotychczas używanymi, z pewnością lub dużym prawdopodobieństwem, nieautentycznymi tytułami)

1 A I **Ballady** op. 23, 38, 47, 52

2 A II **Etiudy** op. 10, 25, Trzy Etiudy (Méthode des Méthodes)

3 A III **Impromptus** op. 29, 36, 51

4 A IV **Mazurki (A)** op. 6, 7, 17, 24, 30, 33, 41, Mazurek a (Gaillard), Mazurek a (z albumu La France Musicale /Notre Temps/), op. 50, 56, 59, 63

25 B I **Mazurki (B)** B, G, a, C, F, G, B, As, C, a, g, f

5 A V **Nokturny** op. 9, 15, 27, 32, 37, 48, 55, 62

6 A VI **Polonezy (A)** op. 26, 40, 44, 53, 61

26 B II **Polonezy (B)** B, g, As, gis, d, f, b, B, Ges

7 A VII **Preludia** op. 28, 45

8 A VIII **Ronda** op. 1, 5, 16

9 A IX **Scherza** op. 20, 31, 39, 54

10 A X **Sonaty** op. 35, 58

11 A XI **Walce (A)** op. 18, 34, 42, 64

27 B III **Walce (B)** E, h, Des, As, e, Ges, As, f, a

12 A XII **Dzieła różne (A)** Variations brillantes op. 12, Bolero, Tarantela, Allegro de concert, Fantazja op. 49, Berceuse, Barkarola; *suplement* – Wariacja VI z „Hexameronu"

28 B IV **Dzieła różne (B)** Wariacje E, Sonata c (op. 4)

29 B V **Różne utwory** Marsz żałobny c, [Warianty] /Souvenir de Paganini/, Nokturn e, Ecossaises D, G, Des, Kontredans, [Allegretto], Lento con gran espressione /Nokturn cis/, Cantabile B, Presto con leggierezza /Preludium As/, Impromptu cis /Fantaisie-Impromptu/, „Wiosna" (wersja na fortepian), Sostenuto /Walc Es/, Moderato /Kartka z albumu/, Galop Marquis, Nokturn c

13 A XIIIa **Koncert e-moll** op. 11 na fortepian i orkiestrę (wersja na jeden fortepian)

30 B VIa **Koncert e-moll** op. 11 na fortepian i orkiestrę (wersja z drugim fortepianem)

14 A XIIIb **Koncert f-moll** op. 21 na fortepian i orkiestrę (wersja na jeden fortepian)

31 B VIb **Koncert f-moll** op. 21 na fortepian i orkiestrę (wersja z drugim fortepianem)

15 A XIVa **Utwory koncertowe** na fortepian i orkiestrę op. 2, 13, 14 (wersja na jeden fortepian)

32 B VII **Utwory koncertowe** na fortepian i orkiestrę op. 2, 13, 14, 22 (wersja z drugim fortepianem)

16 A XIVb **Polonez Es-dur** op. 22 na fortepian i orkiestrę (wersja na jeden fortepian)

17 A XVa **Wariacje na temat z** *Don Giovanniego* **Mozarta** op. 2. Partytura

18 A XVb **Koncert e-moll** op. 11. Partytura (wersja historyczna)

33 B VIIIa **Koncert e-moll** op. 11. Partytura (wersja koncertowa)

19 A XVc **Fantazja na tematy polskie** op. 13. Partytura

20 A XVd **Krakowiak** op. 14. Partytura

21 A XVe **Koncert f-moll** op. 21. Partytura (wersja historyczna)

34 B VIIIb **Koncert f-moll** op. 21. Partytura (wersja koncertowa)

22 A XVf **Polonez Es-dur** op. 22. Partytura

23 A XVI **Utwory na fortepian i wiolonczelę** Polonez op. 3, Grand Duo Concertant, Sonata op. 65

35 B IX **Rondo C-dur** na dwa fortepiany; **Wariacje D-dur** na 4 ręce; *dodatek* – wersja robocza Ronda C-dur (na jeden fortepian)

24 A XVII **Trio na fortepian, skrzypce i wiolonczelę** op. 8

36 B X **Pieśni i piosnki**

37 **Suplement** Utwory częściowego autorstwa Chopina: Hexameron, Mazurki Fis, D, D, C, Wariacje na flet i fortepian; harmonizacje pieśni i tańców: „Mazurek Dąbrowskiego", „Boże, coś Polskę" (Largo), Bourrées G, A, Allegretto A-dur/a-moll

FRYDERYK CHOPIN
POLONAISE in E♭ Op. 22
score

Source Commentary (abridged)
Performance Commentary

SOURCE COMMENTARY /ABRIDGED/

Initial remarks

The present commentary concerns solely the orchestra part (the solo part is discussed in the commentaries to the *Polonaise* in the versions for one piano and with a second piano). It sets out the principles governing the editing of the musical text and discusses the more important discrepancies between sources, as well as signalling the most crucial changes introduced into the printed scores of the *Polonaise* (none of which were published during Chopin's lifetime).

A precise characterisation of all the sources, their relations to one another, a detailed presentation of the differences appearing between them, and also reproductions of characteristic fragments of the different sources are all contained in a separately published *Source Commentary*.

Abbreviations: RH – right hand, LH – left hand. The sign → indicates a relationship between sources, and should be read as 'and the source(s) based thereon'.

Polonaise in E flat major, Op. 22

Sources

[A] The autograph is not extant. It is difficult to state whether the score was written out in full by Chopin or whether – as in the *Concerto in F minor*, Op. 21 – the composer entrusted the notating, and possibly also partly the editing, of the orchestral parts to someone else.

FE First French edition of the version for one piano, M. Schlesinger (M.S.1926), Paris, July 1836. **FE** is based on **[A]** and was proofread by Chopin, probably twice.

PFE Orchestral parts appended to **FE** (same firm and number), most probably prepared from **[A]**. It seems highly unlikely that Chopin contributed to their preparation.

EE First English edition of the version for one piano, Wessel & Cº (W & Cº Nº 1643), London, May 1836. **EE** is most probably based on a proof of **FE** that does not take account of Chopin's final corrections; a number of revisions have been made to the text in this edition, in the preparation of which Chopin did not participate. After 1846 a second impression was issued, with minor alterations. As the NE editors did not discover the orchestral parts prepared by Wessel & Cº, it may be assumed that the orchestral material – as in other Chopin works with orchestra – was not printed by the English publisher.

GE First German edition of the version for one piano, Breitkopf & Härtel (5709), Leipzig, August 1836, based on **FE**. This bears evidence of revisions by the publisher, and also contains a number of errors. Chopin did not participate in its preparation. There exist copies differing in details on the cover (3 versions). After 1852 a second edition was prepared, with minor alterations, and after 1872 its corrected reissue.

PGE Orchestral parts appended to **GE** (same firm and number), most probably based on **PFE**. Some of the errors in the base text were corrected here. There is nothing to suggest Chopin's participation in the preparation of **PGE**.

Sco Manuscript of the score of the *Polonaise* (Österreichische Nationalbibliothek, Vienna), prepared in the 1870s as a base text for its first edition (Breitkopf & Härtel, 1880). The parts of the orchestral instruments were copied from **PGE** and subjected to wholesale revision, primarily in respect to performance markings.

SBH First edition of the score as part of an edition of the complete works of Chopin (*Erste kritisch durchgesehene Gesamtausgabe*), Breitkopf & Härtel (C XII 6), Leipzig 1880. A number of revisions were made here, setting the dynamic and articulation markings in order.

SS Edition of the score of the *Polonaise* prepared by K. Sikorski as part of an edition of the complete works of Chopin, Instytut Fryderyka Chopina and PWM Edition (PWM-3821), Warsaw-Kraków 1961. This was based on **S**BH, with the parts of the violas and double basses arbitrarily added in many places. We take no account of these additions and they are not notated (they are described in detail in the commentary to **S**S).

Editorial principles of the orchestra part

As the base text we adopt **PFE**, as the source which is closest to Chopin's manuscript. We correct clear errors of pitch or rhythm. We set the dynamic and articulation markings in order:

— taking account of the legibility of individual parts and the overall musical sense of the score, we unify markings within groups of instruments and in analogous bars;

— in the *Tutti*, we take account of Chopin's markings in the piano reduction, which is part of the authentic version for one piano.

We transpose the parts of the C clarinets and E♭ horns, as appearing in the original score, for B♭ clarinets and F French horns, most commonly used today.

The piano part comes from volume 32 **B VII** (version for two pianos). We have omitted fingering and elements of notation deriving from the editors which have no effect on the relations between the sound of the solo part and the orchestra (brackets, minor variants).

Polonaise

p. 14

Bars 5-6 The dynamic signs appearing in the sources at the beginning of bar 5 raise doubts: the Vni and Vle have *p*, whilst written in the Vc. and Cb is *f*, which also appears in **FE** (→**EE**, **GE**). The remaining parts have no sign in **PFE** (→**PGE**), and the woodwinds therefore begin the work without dynamic markings, which attests carelessness in this respect.

Given the *crescendos* that fill the subsequent six bars, as well as the possibility of misunderstanding due to the inclusion in the Vc. and Cb. parts of the cue of the French horn signal that opens the *Polonaise*, we regard the *f* in this part as probably erroneous. For this reason, we give *p* for all the instruments that begin their parts in these bars.

Cor. Added at the beginning of bar 5 in **Sco** (→**SBH**) is *p*, after the fashion of additions in the parts of the Ob., Cl. and Fg.

Cor. In **PFE** (→**PGE**→**Sco**) the sign ⸺ begins and ends beneath the 1ˢᵗ note of bar 6, which gives it the appearance of an accent. Regarding the placement and the size of this sign as erroneous, we move it to the second half of bar 5.

Bars 7-8 & 11-13 Vni & Vle. We give the signs ⟨ and *fz*, emphasising the phrasing, on the basis of **FE** (→**EE**,**GE**).

Bar 12 Vni II. On the 3ʳᵈ beat, the sources give quavers f^2-ab^2. As a result, the chord played by the violins and violas on the 5ᵗʰ quaver is not a triad, as is required by Chopin's piano reduction of this place (lack of ab^2); cf. all other chords of bars 11-13.

The note ab^2 was perhaps intended for the Vle – the erroneous writing of 3 ledger lines, instead of 4, is entirely probable. It is also possible that, in order to make the part of the violas easier, this ab^2 was to have been swapped with the f^2 of the second violins, but the change was only introduced in the violas.

Taking all this into account, on the 5ᵗʰ quaver we change the f^2 to ab^2 in the part of the Vni II.

2

p. 15 *Bars 32 & 176* Vle. **PFE** have here *d¹*. This obvious mistake was already corrected to *bb* in **PGE**.

p. 17 *Bar 57* Vni II. Missing in **PFE** (→**PGE**) is the ♮ raising *eb¹* to *e¹*.

Bars 57-58 & 201-202 Vni & Vle. In both places, we give the slurs which **PFE** (→**PGE**) have in bars 201-202. In bars 57-58, added slurs also join the crotchets of bar 57 with the minims in bar 58.

Bars 62 & 206 Vni. In **SS** the crotchets *eb¹* and *g¹* are arbitrarily removed.

Bars 68 & 212 Vle. At the beginning of bar 68 **PFE** (→**PGE**) have a quaver *eb¹*. We give 𝄿 , after the fashion of the other three analogous bars 30, 174 & 212. In **Sco** (→**SBH**) the note was left in bar 68, and the rest was changed to a note in bar 212.

p. 18 *Bars 75-76 & 219-220* Archi. **PFE** (→**PGE**) have here very inconsistent articulation markings. Presented below are all the versions appearing in various parts (discounting minor inaccuracies):

Vni I, bar 75, bar 219, no markings,

Vle, bar 219,

Vc., Cb., bar 219,

other instances.

For the sake of comparison, here are the chords in Chopin's piano reduction in bars 75 & 219:

It is difficult to state how such a variety of notations came about, but it was certainly due to carelessness in the preparation of the parts, as a differentiated performance by particular instruments makes no sense in this context. The following arguments justify the adoption in all the places of a notation with the use of accents alone:
— it is the only notation to appear more than once (in 4 of the 8 places);
— it is not contrary to the other notations (accents appear in all places containing some kind of markings);
— the lack of articulation markings suggests *détaché*, which is the most natural way of playing a polonaise rhythm in a *ff* dynamic.

p. 20 *Bar 105* Vni, Vle, Vc. & Cb. **PFE** (→**PGE**) have here the following dynamic signs: Vni I *p*, Vni II & Vle *pp*. The parts of the Vc. & Cb. have no markings. We unify the dynamics of the violins and violas, giving *pp*, which is notated in a similar context in bar 25 & analog. We also add *p* in the Cb. part – cf. Vc. In bars 91 & 108.

p. 21 *Bar 113* Vni II. Missing in **PFE** is the ♮ raising *ab* to *a*. This obvious mistake was already corrected in **PGE**.

Bars 121-122 Vc. & Cb. In **PFE** (→**PGE**) these parts are notated together. In passages written on a single stave, the use of the double basses in unison with the cellos is clearly marked on each occasion verbally (*Tutti*) or graphically (notation with double stems). In these bars, the notation is one-part, and so the remark *Vcello Solo* that does not appear until bar 123 was probably mistakenly placed 2 bars too late. This conclusion is confirmed in the course of the bass line of the piano part.
Taking this into account, in the Cb. part we give rests in these bars; this solution was also adopted in **SS**, whereas in **Sco** (→**SBH**) the double basses double the part of the cellos.

p. 24 *Bar 150* Vni I. As the last quaver, **PFE** has *bb¹*. This error was already corrected to *ab¹* in **PGE**.

Bar 153 Cb. Read literally, the 1ˢᵗ note should be played *pizzicato*, as the indication arco does not appear in the sources until the last quaver of the bar. However, this is most probably an error:
— the *pizzicato* in bars 149 & 151 are notated in crotchets with the indication pizz., doubtless to emphasise the distinctness of the Cb. part in relation to the other strings (*pizzicato* obtains from bar 133 and is written in crotchets throughout this passage);
— from the beginning of bar 153 the notation alters – the Cb. are notated in quavers *staccato* (then also *legato*), just like the Vc.; if the previous way of playing still applied, the change of notation would be senseless.

p. 25 *Bar 177* Vni II. **PFE** (→**PGE**) have here erroneously *eb¹*, which was corrected to *f¹* in **Sco** (→**SBH**).

p. 28 *Bar 216* Vni II. On the 3ʳᵈ beat **PFE** have erroneously *f¹*.

Bar 221 Cb. **PFE** (→**PGE**) have in this bar a whole-bar rest, which is certainly an error.

Bars 221-261 Vc. & Cb. As the only dynamic markings in this passage, **PFE** (→**PGE**) have *ff* & *pp* in bar 225 and *f* in bar 245. We correct this unquestionable inaccuracy according to the markings written in the parts of the remaining string instruments.

p. 30 *Bar 230* Vni I. At the beginning of the bar, **PFE** have *ab¹*. The error was already corrected to *g¹* in **PGE**.

p. 36 *Bar 279* Timp. In **Sco** (→**SBH**) the marking *tremolo* was added. However, although admissible, this addition does not seem necessary, and so we retain the version of **PFE** (→**PGE**).

Jan Ekier
Paweł Kamiński

3

PERFORMANCE COMMENTARY

The orchestral parts are available for borrowing at the Biblioteka Materiałów Orkiestrowych PWM, ul. Fredry 8, 00-097 Warszawa, tel. +4822-635-35-50, fax +4822-826-97-80, www.pwm.com.pl, e-mail: bmo@pwm.com.pl

General issues regarding the interpretation of Chopin's works will be discussed in a separate volume entitled *Introduction to the National Edition*, in the section *Issues of performance*.

Remarks on the musical text

Editorial additions are written in square brackets [].
L o n g   a c c e n t s denote accents of a primarily expressive character in which the accentuated part generally lasts somewhat longer than in a normal accent (with shorter rhythmic values, it sometimes covers two or three notes), and the drop in the intensity of sound is smoother.

Polonaise in E flat major, Op. 22

p. 14   *Bar 5* We draw attention to the incomplete and unclear dynamic markings in this bar (see *Source Commentary*). Our additions (given in brackets) give the most natural, though not the only, dynamic conception of this place. One may, for example, consider the entry of the basses (Vc., Cb., possibly Fg.) *fzp* or *f*⟩ *p*.

Jan Ekier
Paweł Kamiński